COCKY DOODLE DOO

A BARNYARD COMEDY

REGINALD FOWL

BOOKS BY REGINALD FOWL:

Cocky Doodle Doo (Book 1)
Cocky Doodle Boo (Book 2)
Cocky Doodle Scrooge (Book 3)
Cocky Doodle Woo (Book 4)

CHAPTER ONE

There comes a time when it's appropriate to write one's memoir. As I look back on my life, I find my years have been full of adventures, mysteries, and experiences of a rather colorful nature.

After all, I am a rooster.

We are not meant to be quiet, or to blend in. Not at all. We're meant to stand out, make noise, and fight the good fight, with everything. We're made, by design to be cocky.

Unfortunately, few of us are intelligent enough to read and write, which is why our voices so often go unheard beyond the barnyard. So indulge me, if you will, in sharing mine.

Ah, but where to begin?

I suppose I should start, like any good story, at the beginning.

I was born at a Midwest hatchery in the spring of 2010. My first memories were of intense confinement, trapped in some cylindrical object where I could barely breathe, let alone move. All I knew was that I had to get out.

I began to peck my way out of my imprisonment, bursting through what I later learned was a shell, to find myself in a warm, dark place, surrounded by many others doing the same. They were a golden brown color with white stripes running through patches of black fuzz across their backs.

I looked down at my tiny body to discover that I matched the others.

Brothers and sisters, perhaps?

They gazed back at me just as curious.

We studied one another for a long moment, wondering the same thing.

Where are we? Why are we here?

We huddled close together, afraid, making the only noises we knew how. Small peeps, crying out for help.

Eventually someone came. Large creatures on two legs. Humans, I was soon to learn. Quite a few of them.

A pair of strong hands plucked me from the others, then cleaned me gently, turning me over to examine me.

"I think this one's a boy," he told another. "But I'm not sure."

I began to panic as the other one took me and held me close to his enormous face.

"Sometimes it's hard to tell." He squinted at me with brown eyes the size of the sun. "If you're not sure, just put him in the grab bag."

He handed me back to the first fellow, who shoved me into a box with an assortment of other chicks of all colors—yellow, gray, brown, black, red, you name it. They were unfamiliar to me, or at least, less familiar than the ones I'd just hatched out with.

I shuddered as the box closed.

We were confined again and could feel ourselves moving toward...somewhere.

THE NEXT TWENTY-FOUR hours was full of angst as we embarked on a dark, harrowing ride through what we later discovered was the U.S. Postal system.

I watched through the holes in our small box as we were loaded onto a white truck. It drove from one place to another, tossing us around.

Seeking comfort from the chaos, we pressed closer to each other, too close at times. It was suffocating.

"Let us out!" my companions wailed to no avail, squawking non-stop the entire way.

If I possessed ears like humans, I would have certainly plugged them. The noise was deafening.

Instead, I tucked my head beneath my tiny wing and prayed for deliverance as we were banged about for many miles.

Finally, my prayers were answered when the vehicle came to a halt. None of us moved.

It was dark out and still quite cold at night.

We startled as someone picked us up and carried us into yet another building.

"Just leave them over there," a man said.

Our box was set on a large countertop. A minute later, the door slammed shut.

After my gaggle of newfound companions settled down, everything was eerily quiet. At least till morning, when the sun began to rise and movement stirred nearby.

We all cried out for help. We were hot, hungry, and needed more space.

I heard voices then, as a few other humans came in. I struggled to hear their words over the cacophony of my fellow chicks.

"When is that awful racket going to end?" a female voice said.

"The family is coming to pick them up soon. I called them early this morning," gruffed a deeper voice.

Family? I wondered. What was that?

"Well, they can't come fast enough," the woman replied.

"Tell me about it."

"Shh," I told the others, in a futile attempt to calm them down. "Someone is coming to get us."

"Who?" They began to panic and grew even noisier.

It was at this point I began to realize I was not with a particularly smart batch of my kind. Perhaps that's what I got for being put in the "grab bag."

We all grew hungrier as the time passed and began to squawk louder. Even I could not help myself. I wanted to get away from my crazy cellmates.

At last, someone came and picked up our box. We were on our way once again. But to where?

AFTER MORE BUMPING and banging along, the vehicle stopped. The box opened briefly and four pairs of enormous eyes peered in at us.

My fellow chicks freaked out. "Predators! They're going to eat us!"

I rolled my eyes. "Calm yourselves. We have no idea if they're friend or foe yet."

"Who put you in charge?" a large, fuzzy yellow chick countered. "Do you know something the rest of us don't?"

"I know how to stay calm," I offered.

Though I wasn't sure how much longer that would last as the lid came back down and we began to move again.

My companions cheeped and peeped themselves into oblivion while I watched through the box holes at the passing landscape. Glimpses of green grass and patches of early spring flowers flickered by.

The car finally stopped moving and I gazed outside.

An old white farmhouse stood nearby, flanked by a couple of outbuildings. The structures were encircled by trees whose leaves were just beginning to emerge. Beyond that, bare fields stretched out under pale blue skies in every direction.

We were carried inside a small red building, our box was set down and the lid finally opened.

The room was small but cozy and warm, lined with straw and

shredded paper with strange symbols printed on it. I peered at them, wondering what they meant.

Regardless, the place was much better than a box.

"You see?" I reassured the others. "This isn't so bad."

"It was for him," one of the others said and pointed at a crushed chick.

My heart dropped through the small enclosure that held us and the wooden floor beneath it.

"Is he dead, Dad?" a boy with reddish-brown hair frowned.

The large man sighed. "I'm afraid so. It's a bit of a rough a ride for these little guys. Maybe next time, we'll get them locally instead."

He carefully picked up our deceased companion and set him aside from the flock.

The little girl beside him frowned. "We have to give him a proper burial."

"That's retarded," said her older sister. "It's a chicken, not a person."

I squinted at her. She wasn't the most endearing creature.

"Enough," the man scolded the older girl, then turned to the younger one. "Of course, we can bury him. You're the writer, I'm sure you can pull something together. Maybe a poem or something."

She nodded. "Sure thing."

He pointed at a bag behind him. "Sam, grab that chick feed. I'm sure they're starving."

The boy eagerly grabbed the bag and filled a small feeder, then shoved it toward us.

We plunged into the grains, ravenous, while the farmer poured some fresh water into a matching feeder.

We all took long drinks, refreshing ourselves, then settled down into the shredded newspaper to rest.

Ah, that was much better.

The little girl picked me up gently and stroked my downy coat, then gasped. "He's so soft!"

"They all are," her father said.

She gazed at me and smiled. "Hi. I'm Maggie."

She was an angel. Her hair was like a beautiful coat of feathers, in a shade of bright red. And those eyes—so large and green and lovely. None of us had those. Whatever this creature was, I adored her.

"Pleased to meet you," I peeped back.

It was the only noise I could make.

She held me to her face and squeezed me tight. I gasped for air.

"Thank you, Dad!" she said, then hugged her father while I continued my struggle to breathe.

"Careful now," her father instructed, prying open her hand to give me some relief. "You don't want him to turn out like that other little guy."

The girl's eyes widened. "Sorry, but...Dad! What are we gonna call 'em?"

"Chickens don't need names," sneered her sister.

Ooh, I really didn't like her at all.

"Well of course they do!" Maggie said, as if it was obvious.

"We don't name things we eat," the older girl scolded her.

I looked at the girl, aghast. *Eat?*

Maggie gasped. "We can't eat them! They're our babies!"

Her father took me from her grasp and set me back in the pen with the others, then comforted her. "Melissa is wrong. These chickens are for eggs. Of course, you can name them."

Maggie's face brightened and she wiped her tears. "I can? Thanks Dad!"

"Time to eat!" their mother called from the house.

The boy perked up. "Ooh, what are we having?"

"Fried Chicken!" the mother answered.

I tensed. *Fried what?*

I didn't like that sound of that.

Maggie and her siblings raced back towards the house, passing the farmer's wife as she waddled toward us with a large belly and a small child propped on her hip.

As they entered the hen house, I noticed they both had the same beautiful hair and eyes that Maggie did.

The woman set the small boy down. He bolted towards us, curious.

"These are chickens, Jakey," she said.

He jabbed a chubby finger towards us excitedly. "Kicken!"

She picked up one of the reddish chicks and showed the boy how to pet it. "Gentle, they're small."

The boy of course, nearly pounded the poor thing. She set it down and put the child back on her hip.

"He'll learn," the farmer smiled. "I did."

She took a deep breath and let it out. "I hope so. He's like a bull in a china shop most days. It's exhausting to keep up with him." She rubbed her belly. "And her."

The man bent down and kissed her belly, then stood and kissed her. "Here let me take him."

He lifted him in his arms and pointed to us. "You're not the littlest here anymore. And in a couple more months, you'll be a big brother too."

"Kicken!" Jakey squealed, totally missing the point.

The farmer turned to his wife. "What about Maggie? Do think this will help her?"

I lifted my head and inched closer, listening.

She shrugged. "The school said she doesn't really have any friends. She spends all her time in books."

"Well, now she can spend it with chickens too. It can't hurt at this point."

"She hasn't taken much to the other animals."

"She's just quiet, like me. Besides, chickens are more endearing. And entertaining."

She wagged a finger at him. "That's what you said about the turkeys and look how *that* turned out."

He touched her cheek gently. "Just wait and see, honey."

"If you say so."

7

I smiled as I watched them interact. They seemed like good people.

The couple continued their discussion as they left and headed toward the farmhouse.

I pondered their words.

"Did you hear that?" I asked the others.

"What?" they said.

"The little girl needs a friend."

"A what?"

I sighed, too tired to explain it.

If Maggie needed a friend, I'd be more than happy to volunteer for the job. As for the rest of my companions, they were on their own.

CHAPTER TWO

I t did not take long for the hen house to become our home as we accustomed ourselves to the rhythms of life on the farm.

The mornings were still cool when Bill and Maggie came to feed us and check on us.

We huddled beneath the heat lamp often. The bigger chicks hogged the warmest spots, pushing the rest of us to the outside more and more. As one of the smaller ones, I often ended up in the worst spot, along with a few others.

Our fuzzy down coats began to molt and new feathers grew in their place. Most of us were a strange sight to see.

We shivered as the little girl cleaned our hind ends off, one at a time, every day with warm, wet cloth.

"You don't want to get Pasty Butt," she told us.

I had no idea what that was, but it sounded more dreadful than the cloth, so I obliged.

The others tended to fight her, not wanting anything to do with it.

"Better to just go along and be done with it," I suggested.

"Who put you in charge?" A pale yellow chick huffed and narrowed his dark eyes at me. It was the same one that often challenged me. He was a bit bigger than the rest of us and liked to throw his weight around.

"No one," I replied. "It was merely a suggestion to make things go easier. Take it or leave it."

After Maggie finished cleaning us, she would sit down and read a book to us. It became one of my favorite rituals. I perched on her shoulder as I watched her read the words on the page, marveling at her ability to do so.

I tried to follow by clucking along.

"See, Dad?" she laughed and patted me on the head. "This one is smart."

He grinned. "I've never known a chicken that was smart, at least growing up."

"When will we know if they're boys or girls?" Sam asked as he refilled our water.

Her father blinked for a moment, as if lost in a memory. "Soon. Their feathers should tell us a lot. The boys will get more elaborate combs and tails. In a few months, you'll definitely be able to tell."

Maggie looked up from the book. "Why?"

"Because they'll practically be adults by then."

Sam's brows rose. "That fast?"

Their father nodded. "They're only small for a little while. Enjoy them while you can."

AS OUR FEATHERS EMERGED, so did our personalities. Some were more aggressive than others. I enjoyed their company less and less. I tended to stay near the quieter, smaller chickens like me and tried to leave the bigger ones alone. That didn't always work out, as they soon decided they could push everyone else around.

I escaped by perching in the windowsill, watching for Sam and Maggie to appear and giving a full report of whatever I saw outside to the others. There was a big world out there, and we were still so little. It seemed overwhelming at times.

I could see the farmhouse from here too and would often watch the lights go out one by one at night.

Good night, Maggie, I'd say as her bedroom light winked off. *Sweet dreams.*

During the daylight hours, we were given access to a small, fenced yard where we could play in the dust to our heart's content, and graze on bugs, worms, and whatever else we could find amidst the shade of fruit trees and tall grasses.

It was paradise.

During one such outing, I became aware of other strange creatures watching us from afar.

One of the other chicks glanced at them warily, then back at me. "Who are they?"

"I haven't a clue," I replied. "*What* are they might be a better question."

We called out to one of those strange fellows, who looked back curiously.

None of them answered.

Were they unwilling to talk to us, or unable to?

I watched closely over the next few outings. They seemed to talk to each other, but never to us. Perhaps they didn't know what to think of our kind. Lord knows I didn't at times.

Maybe it was a similar situation to the one we had with the humans. We could understand their words but could not make them. Perhaps these creatures could understand ours but not respond.

I made my way to the edge of the fencing to test my theory. I opened my beak to call out to a large, muscular creature with a long, swishy tale.

But alas, the sun was dipping low and Bill was calling us back inside.

I would have to wait.

THE NEXT DAY, Maggie brought a mirror into the coop. She propped it on the windowsill, then held me up to it, delighting in my new feathers. "Look at how pretty you're becoming!"

I chirped back happily.

Her father looked up from a poultry catalog, studying me for a moment. "I think it's a B.B. Red Old English Bantam." He held up the page. "Look at the feathers they get."

The picture showed a majestic rooster with a red head and a riot of colorful neck feathers, a black breast, and a huge plume of greenish-black feathers for its tail.

My beak dropped open. *That was what I was going to look like? Holy cow.*

Maggie moved close to her father, holding me up towards the picture. "Oh, Dad, he's going to be beautiful."

Her father grinned. "How do you know it's a he?"

"His tail's already starting to come in. Is there any doubt?"

I waggled my new, fluffy tail proudly in the mirror. It was a sight to see.

Maggie put her face next to mine and beamed me a beautiful, toothless smile. She was missing her two front teeth. "Such a distinguished rooster deserves a properly distinguished name."

I smiled as Maggie, Sam, and their father worked their way through several. Richard, Arthur, Archibald, Phineas…they went on for a while.

"How about Reginald?" Sam suggested. "We just read a story in school with a knight named Reginald."

"Reginald," Maggie grinned and kissed my head. "I like it."

I chirped and fluffed out my feathers in approval.

She set me down and did the same with the others, who enjoyed looking at themselves in the mirror. The dumber ones tried to attack it until I explained they were looking at themselves.

One large fellow with black and white spots and beady eyes never did seem to get it.

Maggie studied him closely. "Is there something wrong with this one, Dad? His eyes are strange, like he's suspicious of everyone."

Bill took the bird in his hands and looked at him. "Maybe. I've seen that before." He shrugged. "He's docile enough. Perhaps a bit on the slow side. You're right, though. He does look a bit distrustful. What shall we call him?"

"Ooh! How about Squinty?" Sam piped up.

"Squinty it is."

Their father pointed at the rusty colored chicks. "I think those are Rhode Island Reds. They're a pretty breed, and they lay a lot of eggs."

They were lovely, I thought. Something about red feathers and red hair just did me in.

I watched as he named the reds Lilah, Lucille, and Ginger, hoping they were indeed girls and wouldn't live to regret their names.

Maggie pointed to three large, pale yellow chicks. Fluffy white feathers were emerging from their downy coat, even on their feet. "What are these kind?"

Sam looked over his father's shoulder at the catalog and back at the birds. "Light Brahmas."

Maggie's brows raised as they showed her the picture. "They're going to get so fluffy that they'll look like they're wearing petticoats!"

In celebration of that fact, she named them Princess, Bella, and Sweetie.

"What about this one with feathers all over her head?"

"I think she's a Silkie," her father said.

Sam laughed. "She looks kind of foofy."

I cringed as they decided to name her Foo Foo. It truly was an awful name, though some of Sam's names for us were even worse. He called a Buff Orphington "Biff", the Barred Rock, "Rocky" and a couple of others Lulu, Frankie, and George. He even named one of the Black Australorpes "Barf" until their father made him change it to "Bart."

CHAPTER THREE

After we got our names, the other animals began to approach us while we were out in the yard. The first one was an old gray horse named Henry.

"Greetings," he neighed, nearly giving the flock a heart attack.

I recovered myself and greeted him back. "Hello, my name is Reginald."

I quickly introduced the others.

The horse nodded, seeming pleased. "We were not sure if you were staying or…going."

I stiffened. "Going? We just got here."

The horse explained that there was an unwritten rule on the farm, a pact of sort. Those with names did not associate with those who didn't have names.

"Why not?" the rest of us wondered.

"It's kinder if they are unaware of their fates."

"Why?" Ginger, one of the Reds, asked. "What is their fate?"

Henry looked away, flicking his tail towards a small shed in the distance. "They eat the ones they don't name."

The rest of us gasped.

"Pigs, turkeys, occasionally cows. We weren't sure about you all till they named you."

A memory stirred in my mind of Martha calling the family to dinner. *Fried chicken.*

"Wait," I asked, trying to wrap my mind around it all. "My sweet little Maggie eats animals?"

The horse nodded. "Most humans do. It's just the way of things."

Well, I didn't like that for a second. But I refused to believe that Maggie would do something so cruel. She was the kindest, gentlest of creatures.

I WATCHED for signs of Maggie's hidden, vicious, carnivorous side, but could find none. She and Sam were there bright and early every morning to check on us and refill our food and water. She even helped her father clean out the coop once a week, lining it with newspaper and wood chips. And every night, she tucked us in with a bedtime story as if we were her babies.

How could anyone like that eat a chicken? I wondered.

Though some complained about their new names, we all fared far better than the poor souls who didn't have one at all.

I tried to explain that to the others, but a few of our flock didn't have names yet and that just freaked them out even more.

Eventually Melissa named the others, though her choices were quite odd—Philomena, Myrtle, Jezebel, Lolita, and so forth.

When Maggie pointed out the weird names, Melissa's face turned red.

"Well, you're weird. You spend all your days with your nose in books, reading to chickens."

I moved towards Maggie protectively and crowed at her sister.

"What is he? Your guardian rooster?" she sneered.

"Reginald is my friend," Maggie said defensively.

"Probably your only friend," her sister shot back.

Just then, their mother called them. "Can one of you watch Jakey for a few minutes? I need to lay down for a bit."

Melissa just rolled her eyes. "I wish the baby would hurry up and get here already."

"No, because then she'll cry all the time and you'll wish she hadn't," countered Maggie. "And Mom will need even more help."

Melissa groaned.

"Girls?" their mother called out to them.

"I'll take him," Maggie volunteered, picking me up and placing me on her shoulder. We strolled towards the farmhouse and retrieved Jakey.

Maggie set us both under a large maple tree and held up a book of ABCs.

"Time for school," she said in a singsong voice. "You two can learn together."

The little boy smiled, his green eyes dancing excitedly. The resemblance to his sister was unmistakable.

"Kicken!" he squealed, squeezing me a bit too hard.

I protested and he relaxed his grip.

"Careful," Maggie warned, then sat down and pulled us both onto her lap.

She opened the book and began reading, pointing at the letters and numbers.

Jakey repeated after her. "A…B….C…"

I tried to follow along, but could only manage a ridiculous crow. "Bawk, bawk, bawwwwwk!!!!"

They looked at each other and laughed, then squeezed me tight. "Good job, Reginald!"

I was in heaven.

BOOKS BECAME a great joy to me, and soon the strange symbols on the paper began to make sense.

What an amazing feeling when I discovered that I, too, could read.

I clucked along happily as Maggie read the stories. Jakey followed along too.

Maggie laughed. "You're not like the other chickens, are you Reg?"

Heavens, I should hope not, I thought.

My flock seemed a bit jealous when I returned to the hen house. They quizzed me relentlessly.

"What did you do?"

"What did they say?"

"Did you eat?"

On and on they went.

Every. Single. Time.

The other roosters started acting crazy. They'd become much more aggressive lately. They would compete for the girl's attention by seeing who could crow the loudest and strut the prettiest.

They didn't want any competition, so they started to bully each other, particularly us smaller ones.

Out of all of us, Speedy was the smallest. He was a Silver Duckwing, an Old English Bantam breed like me. He had the same black breast and fluffy greenish-black tail, but instead of a red head and multicolored neck feathers, he had a shock of silvery white ones that trailed gloriously all the way down his back. His comb was bright red and nearly as big as his head. He was quite striking and a prime target for the bullies.

Luckily for him, his size allowed him to fly when most of the others grew too heavy, and his long, skinny legs carried him faster than any of the others, keeping him out of harm's reach. He'd missed out on several beatings that way.

I, on the other hand, was not quite so fortunate. I wasn't fast enough to escape my fellow roosters' wrath.

If there was a pecking order, I was at the bottom of it.

I often retreated into a corner to read the papers that lined the hen house. They kept me informed and distracted till I could go outside again and discuss current events with the horse. He seemed to enjoy that as much as I did. It was nice to have friends, even if they weren't from my flock. Maybe that was a bonus.

"What did the guys do this time?" Henry asked, concerned.

"Just the usual," I sighed wearily. "Shoving, pecking, stomping."

We roosters were also waking up before dawn. For some reason, the appearance of the sun made us want to crow till our lungs fell out. The ladies, not so much, but every one of us guys started doing it. We couldn't help it. There were seven of us back then, and we were all cackling our heads off, seeing who could crow the loudest. The other animals complained about the noise. I guess we were lousy neighbors.

Surprisingly, the farmer didn't mind at all. He seemed to expect it.

Some of the bigger chickens crowed all day long—Sweetie, Rocky, and Biff were the worst. Speedy and I only felt like doing it in the morning.

One and done, we'd say.

Perhaps it was because we were from calmer breeds and didn't feel the need to compete so much. That's what the poultry catalog said. Bill had left it in the coop and I'd read it cover to cover one day after a particularly bad thrashing.

Maybe we were just happier with who were to begin with. I just wished the others didn't work so hard to make us miserable.

IF ALL THAT wasn't enough, the girls started laying eggs one day.

Lucille stood up and an egg dropped right out from underneath her.

We were all in shock.

"Ouch!" she screamed. "What the heck was that?! A baseball?"

She was none too happy at first, till the other hens did it too. Soon they started singing every time they did it.

I admit, the tunes were rather catchy, and we'd all be sucked into singing along and cheering them on.

"Lucille just laid an egg!" We'd all cluck.

"And so did our Foo Foo!
Princess and Bella,
Now they've got eggs too!
Eggs, eggs, eggs! Go, ladies, go!
We're rooting for you!
Philomena, Rosarita, Lilah, Ginger too!
Bart and Frankie, Georgie Girl, and of course, Lulu!
Eggs, eggs, eggs! Go, ladies, go!
Cocky Doodle Doo!
Cocky Doodle Doo!"
On and on it went.

Even Squinty sang along. Kind of.

It became one of my favorite times of the day. No one fought. Ever. We were too happy singing about all those wondrous eggs.

Why? We had no clue.

We never heard the ducks or geese raising the roof in song about their eggs. I guess it was just a chicken thing, or we were so loud we drowned all the others' songs out.

Maggie and Sam came soon after and collected the eggs from the nesting boxes, their eyes wide.

"Wow! What is mom gonna do with all these?" Sam asked in astonishment. "We'll be eating them forever!"

"She could share with neighbors, like we do the milk," Maggie suggested. "Mr. Hall down the road turns it into cheese."

"Yeah, but what can you turn eggs into? Besides more eggs?"

Maggie thought for a moment, then shrugged. "I'm sure mom will figure something out. Come on, we have to hurry before Melissa beats us back and eats all the bacon."

The boy startled, nearly dropping an egg as he scurried out of the hen house.

Maggie opened the small side door to let us into our yard, then said her goodbyes. "See you later, chickies!"

She raced off to join her brother, laden down with a heavy basket of eggy plunder.

CHAPTER FOUR

S ummer began to bloom on the farm, warm and glorious.

I was in our yard, feasting on the first of the mulberries, when Ginger came up next to me.

"Hello," I smiled, offering her a berry. "Would you like some? They're quite tasty."

"Hello," she smiled back, but did not appear interested in the berries. She just stared at me.

I checked myself over, wondering if my feathers were in disarray or if something had gotten stuck to my backside.

"What is it?" I finally inquired.

"You're just so, so….beautiful," she sighed.

I blinked at her. "Really?"

Despite Maggie's assurances, my colors hadn't turned out to be a good thing. The guys had picked on me mercilessly about them. The hens had never said anything about them at all. I assumed they thought I was ugly or garish. Until now.

"All of those lovely colors make you look like a rainbow. And then when you start talking…" she sighed again. "Well, you are the most beautiful thing I've ever seen. A Rainbow Rooster."

I shifted from foot to foot, uncomfortable with the attention. "Thank you, fair lady. You are quite lovely yourself."

The next day in the barnyard, the other girls started following me around, too.

"Ooh, you're so pretty," they all swooned.

"But not as stunning as you, darlings," I replied. "Allow me to bask in your beauty."

They swooned again.

I read them some poetry, which made them swoon even more. "Oh Bird, thou never wert..."

I spent the afternoon by the mulberry bush, soaking up the sunlight and telling them stories from the books Maggie had read to me. Chicka Chicka Boom Boom and Green Eggs and Ham were their favorites. They hung on my every word and batted their eyes at me.

I smiled to myself. I was a rooster with a colorful tail telling... colorful tales.

Later, we ran around the barnyard, playing tag and hide and seek, like we'd seen Bill's kids do.

Of course, I was easily found and always lost the game. My feathers drew far too much attention. But the adoration of the ladies made my spirit soar and my heart sing, and I felt like a winner every time.

I sighed happily and thought, *Oh, how I love being a Rainbow Rooster.*

BUT SOMETIMES BEAUTY WAS A CURSE. The other roosters did not appreciate all of the attention I was receiving from the ladyfolk.

I was returning to the hen house late one afternoon after an extended poetry reading near the mulberries, when Sweetie, Biff, Rocky, and Bruce surrounded me on all sides, ruffling their feathers and eyeing me menacingly.

"Is there a problem, gentlemen?" I asked, but before I could say or do anything, they leapt on me, all at once, crowing, pecking, tearing at me with their talons.

I squawked in protest as they began plucking my beautiful tail feathers out one by one.

"Pretty boy needs a lesson in the pecking order," Sweetie said. "The girls don't belong to you."

"They don't belong to anyone," I replied. "They can spend their time with whomever they choose."

But my response did not please them, and only earned me a good whooping.

The girls stood by, frozen in horror.

"No one's coming to your rescue now, Freak," snarled Sweetie, who was anything but sweet.

"She" proved to be a "he" and had grown to be enormous. After watching Sesame Street with Jakey once, I came to regard Sweetie as an evil, fluffy, white Big Bird.

"You think you're better than the rest of us, but we'll fix that."

The larger boys took turns jumping on me, scratching me, and tearing out the rest of my lovely feathers. They even pecked my comb!

Except Squinty, who just stared blankly, like he always did. The lights were on, but no one was home.

As I lay on the ground, bruised and bleeding, I lost count of the times they hit me and stomped on me.

I had no idea where Speedy had disappeared to, but I could hear Lucille, Ginger, and the rest of the girls crying, begging them to stop before everything faded to black.

I AWAKENED to see the face I loved most.

Maggie looked at me with huge green eyes full of concern. They looked redder than normal, as if she'd been crying.

We were in the barn, with the cows and geese, who looked just as worried.

Beatrice mooed a hello and the geese honked.

"Oh, Reg, I'm glad you're okay," Maggie said as she cleaned my wounds with a warm cloth, just like she'd cleaned my bum when I was little.

She put some kind of smelly ointment on them, then picked me up gently and cradled me like a baby, turning tear-filled eyes to her father. "Why did the other roosters hurt him, Dad?"

Bill leaned against the door frame and sighed. "It's what roosters do. Sometimes they're okay if they're raised together, sometimes not. I'm afraid I may have to cull them so we don't have so many fighting."

She looked at him, alarmed, and clutched me tighter to her chest. I could hear her heartbeat racing.

"You mean eat them?" she asked, horrified.

Her father nodded. "They will fight to the death, until they establish a pecking order. That's their way."

"But not my Reginald," she said and squeezed me tighter. I could scarcely breathe. "He's so gentle and smart."

"He is becoming what nature intended him to be, a rooster. And if he doesn't learn to stand up for himself, he might not survive."

Maggie blinked at him for a moment. "Does the same go for people, too?"

Her father furrowed his brow at her, not understanding. "What do you mean?"

She lowered her eyes to the floor and did not answer.

"Maggie, is someone bullying you at school?"

She nodded, tears streaming down her face.

"Who?"

"There's this boy named Roger. He sits behind me. He's always kicking me and pulling my hair. Sometimes he gets me in trouble. And the girls see him doing it, and they start in on me too."

"Maybe they're just jealous of that beautiful red hair," her father smiled. "Your mother got teased like that when she was your age and look at her now."

He did have a point. Martha was lovely for a human. Almost as lovely as my Reds.

"Why don't they like me?" she cried. "What did I do wrong?"

"Nothing," her father reassured her. "You're different. You're special. Like Reginald here. To some people, that's a threat. They're jealous. You have to learn to stand up for yourself, just like Reginald does."

"I just want him to leave me alone!" she said.

I looked at her sadly. I knew exactly how she felt.

School would be out for her soon, bringing some relief. I knew Maggie was looking forward to that. But what about next year and the year after that?

Did it just go on and on?

I hoped not, for both our sakes.

CHAPTER FIVE

I spent two weeks in the barn recovering from my injuries and got to know its inhabitants quite well. I did miss my lady friends but found the company of the cows surprisingly refreshing.

Beatrice, Buttercup, and Moo had been on the farm for a long time and had plenty of entertaining stories to tell, especially about Maggie as a baby, and even Melissa, which surprised me.

"Melissa doesn't seem very nice, to anyone," I remarked.

"She actually very sweet, just confused," Beatrice said.

"Why?"

"She's becoming a teenager," Moo explained. "They have no idea what they want or how to act. She talks to us while she milks us in the mornings. Right now, she likes a boy that doesn't know she exists."

"Ah, young love," Buttercup said. "Apparently Martha had the same problem with Bill when they met."

Martha was beautiful. How could Bill not notice her?

I shook my head. I did not understand humans sometimes.

"Whatever happened to the turkeys?" I asked. "Martha mentioned them but I haven't actually seen any."

"Oh, they're still here," Moo smiled mysteriously.

Buttercup kicked her.

"Ouch!"

I got the feeling that whatever had befallen them was off limits for discussion.

I began to recite some of my hen house haikus for a much needed change of subject.

"The cock crows
At the gold and peach dawn
A summer serenade."

"Yes," Moo smiled. "We can hear you sometimes from way over here."

"We are rather loud," I admitted.

I put my head under my wing, feeling horribly embarrassed.

"We like youuuu," Beatrice lowed. "Though the jury is still out on the others."

"Our ladies are wonderful," I said, feeling the need to defend them. "But some of the males leave a lot to be desired."

"What about that little guy who's always in the tree?"

"That's Speedy. He's a bit flighty and unfortunately small. He gets picked on even more than I do. He would do well to acquire some bigger friends to keep him out of trouble."

"Well, he's always welcome here," Moo offered.

"Forgive me for asking, but how on Earth did you come to be called, Moo?" I asked the poorly named cow.

She smiled. "Sam named me."

"Well, that explains a lot."

"He was three. And so cute," she sighed wistfully. "Jakey looks just like him."

I grinned. Maggie and Jakey came to the barn every day to read to me. The cows and the geese also enjoyed it.

"They grow up so fast," Buttercup said. "Henry remembers Bill at that age."

The revelation surprised me. "Really?"

Moo nodded. "The farm has been in Bill's family for ages. Ask

Henry some time. He loves to tell the stories. His mate Betsy passed away last year. He's been a bit lonely. He needs to feel useful once in a while."

"I think we all do," I agreed.

I made a mental note to visit the old horse again as soon as I could.

SCHOOL WAS FINALLY OUT for Maggie and she no longer had to deal with her bully, at least for now. But I was preparing to face mine again.

I was hesitant about going back to my flock, especially after spending so much enjoyable time in the barn.

I said my goodbyes to my new companions and promised to come back soon—uninjured.

Maggie and Jakey read to me under our favorite tree that afternoon, then put me back in the hen house.

The chickens kept to themselves for the most part, greeting me with a cold shoulder, or tail feather. I had no idea what had gone on in my absence, but they all seemed rather skittish.

It didn't take long to find out why.

Sweetie had been on a tear lately, appointing himself head rooster and beating up anyone who would challenge him. The others began hiding in the yard and trees to avoid persecution.

When Sweetie wasn't watching, the flock greeted me warmly and asked me how my stay in the barn was. I filled them in.

"You must meet the other animals. Did you know Henry has been here the longest? He knows all about the history of the farm. He came to live here when Bill was a child. He said Bill was very quiet, like Maggie, but always getting into trouble. He and his brother Bob were rather mischievous. One day they took an old car battery and zapped him in the—"

I glanced around at the eager faces of my flock, prepared to tell them the entire story, when I noticed that some of us were missing. "Wait, weren't there thirty of us?"

The others looked at me blankly. None of them could count.

"Someone's missing."

More than one, I thought as I began to count. I lost track several times and had to start over. I'd been practicing with Jakey, and didn't think I'd missed any numbers, but wanted to be sure.

No, there were thirty of us before I was attacked. Now there were twenty-seven. Who was missing?

I began to run through them by breed. All the Reds were here, thank heaven. So were the Brahmas, the Barred Rocks, the Old English...

"Philomena's disappeared."

"Who?" Rocky asked.

"The Black Australorpe."

"She's probably outside in a tree," Sweetie approached, glaring at me menacingly. "Maybe I should put you up there with her."

I ignored his threat. "She's too big for the tree. Only us smaller ones can get up there now."

That brought me to the other two missing chickens. Speedy and Squinty.

Speedy was small enough, and high-strung enough, to be up in a tree.

The fact that he hadn't given himself a heart attack yet was a small miracle in itself.

Squinty could be anywhere. He often stopped and stared at things for hours. He came inside much later than the rest of us. It took him a while to catch on. Some days I was amazed he could remember how to breathe.

But it was too late to go looking for him. We were locked up for the night.

I just hoped they would be alright till morning.

As if on cue, something growled outside, making us startle.

Just why were we locked inside every night?

What was out there?

Whatever it was, I hoped I never had to come face-to-face with it. Dealing with Sweetie was bad enough.

THE NEXT DAY, I found Squinty outside, still staring at the door like he had the night before. Speedy was hiding in his favorite tree like usual.

"Have you seen Philomena?" I asked him.

"No, but there were strange noises last night. I thought it was Squinty at first, but he just stood stone still the entire time."

I shook my feathered head. "Something's not right. We need to keep our eyes open."

"For Squinty?" Speedy asked, confused.

"For predators," I told him.

The little rooster shook so hard he nearly fell out of the tree.

CHAPTER SIX

After the beatings I'd received, I had to keep the poetry on the down low. None of the hens seemed particularly interested in learning how to read, but they loved listening to me read. It was a start.

The girls and I would rendezvous near the mulberries as often as we could. Speedy kept watch above us in the trees in case Sweetie, Biff, or the others caught wind of our activities.

I knew I was asking for trouble, but who could resist a lady hen? A rooster is born to keep them happy, as well as safe. With my favorite ladies close by, I could entertain them and assure their safety as well.

"Oh Reginald," Ginger swooned. "Read it again!"

The ladies had also taken a liking to my impromptu hen house haikus and rhymes.

"Roses are red,
And so are your feathers.
I love you, fair ladies,
In all kinds of weather."

I started to regale them with a rousing tale about pirates and stolen treasure when another fight broke out, this time between

Rocky and Sweetie. I moved to stop it, but they just tossed me aside and continued fighting.

"Idiots!" I squawked at them. "Don't you understand that the farmer will get rid of some of us if we don't stop fighting?

Sweetie, who held Rocky by the throat with his talons, stopped and looked at me. "What are you talking about?"

"I overhead the farmer say if we don't stop fighting, he will eat us."

The girls gasped in shock.

"Not you lovelies, you're safe," I reassured them. "You lay delicious eggs and strut around looking splendid all day. But the guys, that's a different story. Bill thinks there are too many of us, and that's why we fight. He's probably right."

"Who is Bill?" Rocky choked, still in a stranglehold.

"The farmer, Maggie's father."

"You're bluffing," Sweetie said, and went back to pounding Rocky's head against the fence. "We fight, it's what we do."

"Well, you'll be fighting your way out of a stew pot if you don't stop!" I warned them.

DESPERATE, I snuck out to visit my friends in the barn and the stalls, trying to figure out what to do. I brought Speedy with me and introduced him to Henry.

They were complete opposites.

Henry was big, old, and slow.

Speedy was small, young, and fast.

Both seemed to have an affinity for old, lame jokes, which they bonded over.

"What does an evil hen lay?" Henry asked us.

I stared at him for a moment, befuddled. I'd never met a hen I didn't like, let alone an evil one.

"Deviled eggs!" Henry smirked.

Speedy fell over laughing. "Ooh, that's good! How about this one: What do you call a horse that lives next door?"

"A neigh-bor!" Henry cracked up. "That's an oldie but a goodie."

I cringed. "That's awful."

"That's what makes it so great! Hey, how about this one—"

On and on they went. I never heard the end after that.

But there were more pressing things at hand.

"Henry, Bill mentioned culling us roosters because we fight too much," I asked solemnly. "Do you think he'd actually do that?"

Henry's smiled faded. "There are plenty of animals here that end up on the dinner table, the ones with no names."

"Yes, but we all have names."

"I don't think a name is much protection if someone's causing trouble. We had chickens here when Bill was small. They were very rowdy. His father had to kill quite a few of the males before the flock settled down. I don't think they ever had more than one or two roosters after that."

Speedy swallowed a lump in his throat and begin pacing nervously, looking for a tree to escape into. "But there are seven of us right now."

I nodded. It didn't bode well. "We have to get the others to stop fighting, before it's too late."

"I'm not sure you can," Henry admitted.

I sighed. That was exactly what I was worried about.

THE NEXT DAY I was back in the mulberries with the girls reciting Shakespeare, when I sensed an unwelcome presence.

I stopped for a moment and listened. "What was that?"

"What was what?" Foo Foo asked, her feathers in her face. "I can't see a thing."

A huge bird circled overhead.

"I'm sorry, ladies, we'll have to finish this later." I looked up to Speedy's perch and called to him.

He peered down at me, annoyed. "What?"

I motioned skyward. "We've got company."

His enormous red comb shook nervously. "Wh-What is that, Reg?"

"A chicken hawk. Come down and help me get the girls inside, especially the smaller ones."

He sped down the tree, flying by in a blaze of feathers.

We hustled the girls inside, clucking and crowing the entire way.

Rocky, Biff, and Bruce followed us, mightily confused.

We entered the hen house to find Sweetie stuffing his face full of chicken feed. The big bully ate more than the rest of us combined.

He stopped and turned his beady brown eyes on me. "What are you going on about now?"

Speedy tried to explain but he spoke so fast no one could understand him. I opened my mouth to intervene.

"I swear you two never shut up," he ruffled his feathers. "Always prattling on about something!"

I tried to explain. "There's a large hawk outside. They eat chickens."

"Most of us are too big for them to carry off now."

"Not us smaller ones," I pointed out. "The owls enjoy snacking on us too, which is why we shouldn't be outside at night. And if you haven't noticed, so do foxes, skunks, opossums, coyotes, neighbor dogs, and raccoons."

Sweetie narrowed his eyes at me and stepped forward menacingly. "What's your point?"

"Everything around here wants to eat us!"

The girls began to freak out.

"Don't worry, we'll protect you. As roosters, it's our job to give our lives defending yours, but we'd do that better if we stopped trying to kill each other."

"You're just paranoid because you're little and you get stomped a lot," Sweetie said.

"No, I just enjoy not being someone's dinner." I groaned in frustration. "What do you think happened to Philomena? What do you think will happen to the rest of us? We'd be much safer if we worked together to fight these predators rather than letting them pick us off one by one."

"You read too many books," Sweetie snarled, turning his attention back to the feeder.

By the time everyone went back outside, the hawk was gone and I was accused of having a vivid imagination.

BUT SURE ENOUGH, three more hens went missing the next day. Both Blue Andalusians—Penelope and Lolita—and poor Bart, the sweet but badly named Buff Orphington.

I feared for the fate of my lady friends and began asking around the farm.

"Did you see anything last night?" I asked the pigs first.

They couldn't give me much information. They were too busy wallowing in the mud and sleeping to notice what was going on outside their pen.

So I asked the cows.

"We were here in the barn," said Beatrice. "I heard some howling. Maybe the neighbor dog."

I asked Henry. "No, the neighbor dog doesn't bark like that. Maybe a coyote."

I froze. We didn't stand a chance against wild dogs of any kind. What could we do? We were the smallest animals on the farm. How on earth could we defend ourselves?

I asked the geese.

"Coyotes usually gang up and attack all at once, not one by one," Hans said. "They may have been howling, but I bet you were dealing with something smaller."

That was the first heartening news I'd heard.

"Could be a fox," Greta suggested.

My heart sank. They were too big and fast for us.

"But it could also be a raccoon or an opossum. You might have a fair chance of beating one of those."

I was feeling hopeful again when Hans added, "Or a skunk. Ooh, that could go badly."

"But wouldn't we have smelled him a mile away?"

"True, that," the gander replied. "Either way, you all need to get yourselves organized and learn how to defend yourselves."

"How on earth do we do that?"

Greta leaned towards me conspiratorially. "Talk to the duck."

"You mean Lucky? That weird Peking duck that walks around talking to himself all day?"

Hans nodded. "The one and only."

"Alright," I groaned.

I was growing tired of interrogating the entire farm. I just wanted some answers and was willing to listen to anyone at this point.

"COME ALONG, SPEEDY." I called up into the tree in the chicken yard. "It's time we took matters into our own hands—or rather, wings."

He climbed down hesitantly. "What can we do? We're too small to do much."

"We're going to see a duck."

"A duck?"

"About martial arts."

"Martial what?"

For a quiet rooster, he sure did ask a lot of questions.

"Why do we need to learn martial arts? Are you sure it's okay to sneak out? Won't Bill be worried? What about Maggie? What if something eats us on the way back?"

I'd never heard him talk so much the entire time I'd known him.

Usually, he was too scared to say anything, except to Henry.

We arrived at the duck's tiny home near the back pond. It was an old doghouse.

"Cozy," I said, though it seemed a bit small to do any kind of practicing in.

"Ah, greetings," Lucky said. "Hans told me you might stop by. You are seeking to learn the Way of the Duck."

"Well, actually, we're seeking to learn the way of not being eaten."

"Same thing," the duck shrugged. "Come. We will practice in the *dojo*."

"What's a *dojo*?" Speedy asked.

"Not what, but where."

Lucky led us into the barn, up a flight of stairs and into the loft. "Here is where you will learn. But first, you must discipline your mind."

That didn't sound so bad, but I wasn't sure how that would help with predators.

"You will learn to use your body and mind together to defend and protect yourselves and others."

He spun, kicked, and danced across the floor of the barn loft.

"Wow," Speedy said. "I've never seen a duck move like that."

No one had. In fact, I was having trouble following along. "You don't have a book of these moves, by any chance?"

"Um, no," Lucky said, tapping his temple. "You must memorize them."

"But where did you learn them?"

"From my father, and his father before him. My family has a proud tradition. We hail from China."

"What do you call this form of martial arts again?" I asked.

"*Tae Kwon Duck*," he said.

"I thought that was Korean."

Lucky nodded. "It is. Sort of. We picked it up along the way here and made it our own. *Tae* means foot, *Kwon* means fist. We use them both to fight smarter, not harder."

He showed us the different positions once again while chanting, *"Hana, dul, set, net, dasot, yasot, ilgop, yodol."*

"Yodel?" I asked. "As in singing?"

I had no idea what he was saying or doing.

"I'm counting through the steps," he explained. "Now it's your turn."

That was easier said than done. I was far better with the written word. Give me an instruction manual any day.

Speedy, however, seemed to get right into it. He was fast and took to it like a bird to…well, he took right to it.

"Good posture, good stance. You're a natural," Lucky said approvingly. "You'll have it down in no time."

Lucky worked us mercilessly every afternoon, like a drill sergeant. I had to forsake precious time with the ladies to hone my skills, but in the end, it was all for them anyhow.

Soon he had us counting up to twenty in Korean, with matching stances for each number.

We practiced hard, sparring with Lucky and then with each other.

Speedy beat me nearly every time.

I collapsed, exhausted. This was much harder than reciting poetry in mulberry bushes, which after the first hour or two, was actually a lot of work.

Speedy, however, barely broke a sweat.

"I've never seen such fast reflexes," Lucky told me.

"Well, he drinks a lot of coffee," I joked.

Lucky looked at me, perplexed. "What's coffee?"

"Oh, never mind."

AFTER WEEKS OF TRAINING, we were ready for any predator that might come our way— fowl, canine, or otherwise.

The first test of my newfound skills was a challenge by Rocky. He had been picking up Sweetie's bad habits.

He grabbed me by the throat in the hen house, seeking to bash my head against the water feeder.

I caught him off balance and flipped him over, then took up a battle stance.

"*Shi-jak!*" I screamed, which meant "ready" in Tae Kwon Duck.

Rocky gawked at me. "What? Did you read a book about samurais or something?"

I was surprised Rocky even knew what one was.

He was dumber than a rock, and about as tough as one too, as several of my blows bounced right off of him.

Uh oh, I thought. This might not have been a good idea.

Rocky swung at me with his wing, and I ducked out of the way, regaining my balance.

I stepped forward and counted through the numbers, using every posture to kick and punch him. "*Hana, dul, set, net...*"

This time, it worked. He was tossed off balance and struggled to get up. I used his weight against him to keep him down.

The girls watched with beaks ajar, astounded as I knocked Rocky out with a roundhouse kick to the head.

I glanced around the hen house, eyes narrowed. "Anyone else?"

The other roosters just stared at me in shock, looking like Squinty.

The girls swooned.

"How did you do that?" Ginger asked, impressed.

"Would you like me to show you some moves?" I offered.

She batted her eyelashes at me. "Perhaps behind the mulberry bush..."

"Ah, but alas, there are no more berries left."

"Who cares," she said and dragged me off to the bushes.

The other ladies followed close behind, and soon we were conducting Tae Kwon Duck classes back there, too.

They learned quickly, and what made them happy, made me happy.

Did I mention that I love being a rooster?

CHAPTER SEVEN

I was preparing for my morning crow-a-thon early one midsummer's day, a cool breeze drifting through the upper screens of the hen house when I heard Martha yelling.

I flew up to the coop window and peered out, curious.

Bill was escorting his wife to the car. She could barely walk. She stopped and clutched her belly, which was now enormous, her face contorted in pain.

"Something is wrong with Martha," I told the others. "She looks like she's dying."

Speedy flew up to the window beside me. "She sounds like it, too."

We watched with concern as Bill herded her into their large vehicle, then tossed a pink suitcase into the back.

My beak dropped open. Was he getting rid of her?

Another car pulled up and two people with silvery hair emerged from it.

I had never seen them before, but they resembled Bill. I wasn't sure though. To me, humans all looked a bit similar.

The man and woman talked to Bill for a few minutes, then went inside the farmhouse, presumably to care for the children.

Bill jumped into the car and sped off with Martha, leaving a cloud of dust behind them.

Where were they going in such a hurry?

The yelling, the suitcase, Martha's face…they all came together in my mind and formed the most terrible of possibilities.

"Bill's getting rid of Martha!" I cried.

The others looked at me, wide-eyed. "No!"

It was an affront to all roosters. We would never dream of disposing of our ladies, but humans did strange things sometimes. If they were capable of eating chickens, they were capable of anything, though I could scarcely bring myself to believe it. Bill was always such a nice man.

My worst fears were compounded when Maggie and Sam did not come that morning to greet us, refresh our food, and gather eggs.

The whole world seemed topsy turvy.

What on earth was going on?

I SPENT the morning sulking over Maggie's mother.

Goodbye, Martha, I thought sadly. *I did not know you well, but you were so sweet, like my Reds.*

My heart ached. How could Bill dispose of her? She was a good mother to the children. They would be devastated.

I ruffled my feathers at the thought. Something inside of me could not let it rest.

You cross the people I love, you cross me, I thought.

It was then that I resolved to avenge Martha and kill Bill.

Yes, he had been very good to us, but if that was how he was going to treat his women, he didn't deserve to live. I would consider him a predator.

Speedy was in complete agreement with me. "I hate to say it, but Bill's gotta go."

Perhaps we had been reading too many stories, but we didn't care. No one treated a lady that way. He would have to pay.

So, we slipped off to the dojo and spent the morning brushing up on our Tae Kwon Duck.

Bill was big and would be hard to take down. If we coordinated our attack, we'd stand a better chance.

Lucky arrived and watched, astounded at our intensity. "Wow, you two are really taking your training seriously."

We said nothing. There was probably a jail for chickens who killed humans, or a stew pot.

He was better off if he didn't know what we were up to. Then no one could accuse him of being an accessory to murder.

We continued to practice all morning and into the afternoon, then returned to the coop, exhausted.

THERE ARE times in life when one is totally, utterly wrong about something.

This is not always a bad thing, as long as you catch it in time.

Our worst fears about Martha were assuaged that afternoon as Speedy and I lay in the shaded part of the chicken yard, dog-tired.

"How are we supposed to take on a human when we can barely take on each other?" he asked.

I tried to summon up the will power to form a coherent reply when Maggie and Sam came running out of the house yelling, "It's a girl! It's a girl!"

Speedy looked at Maggie, aghast. "She's celebrating the replacement of her mother?"

I watched in horror as Maggie jumped the fence, grabbed me, and danced around. "I have a new little sister, Reg! Her name is Lacey. She's coming home with Momma tomorrow."

I breathed a sigh of relief and nestled into Maggie's shoulder.

"Martha's not being replaced," I clucked at Speedy. "She's having a baby."

"A what?"

"She laid an egg. A really big one."

"Oh." He scratched his comb, deep in thought. "Then why'd they go away?"

"I haven't a clue, but they're coming back, and they're bringing it with them."

I smiled. Another little addition was coming to the farm. "I guess we don't have to kill Bill now."

"Thank God," he said and flopped over.

Later, the cows and geese informed us that humans did not hatch like we did. They were born.

"What's born?" we asked.

"They come out of their mother like an egg, but bigger, and no shell," Greta the goose explained.

We gasped. No wonder Martha had been in so much pain.

Buttercup chuckled. "She'll be fine."

I wasn't so sure, but it gave me new respect for human females.

MARTHA RETURNED with the baby and did indeed appear to be fine. The large bulge in her belly had disappeared. Now, she carried it in her arms.

Lacey was a tiny pink lump that cried all day long.

None of us were very impressed.

"What is that awful noise?" Foo Foo complained, lifting the feathers from her eyes. "

"That is a baby," I explained. "A human baby."

"Geez," said Lulu. "They sound worse than the loons down at the duck pond."

"Tell me about it. She sounds like a foghorn."

"A what?" Ginger asked.

"Never mind."

Martha brought Lacey out one day during story time beneath the tree.

"That's a baby," Maggie told me.

I peered at Lacey curiously.

She seemed less frightening up close. She was small and soft and round, with a little tuft of red hair that matched her mother's and sister's.

"Baby!" squealed Jakey.

Lacey startled and began to cry.

I cringed at the noise.

Martha sighed and tried to settle her down again. She looked exhausted, but despite everything, she appeared to be in good spirits.

Bill doted on her constantly.

Speedy and I felt bad for plotting to kill him.

We decided he was a good fellow, but should he ever turn, we would stand at the ready.

After all, a lady was a lady, regardless of species. We would protect them, one and all, no matter what.

CHAPTER EIGHT

The baby grew as the summer sailed by and the days began to grow shorter.

Maggie sat under our favorite tree with me and Jakey one mid-August day, struggling to get through Chicka Chicka Boom Boom for the thousandth time.

I looked up to see her crying.

What's wrong? I wondered.

"School starts next week," she finally said. "And I'll have to face Roger again."

I nestled into her shoulder and her beautiful red hair, reassuring her.

"Courage, my friend," I clucked.

I knew she could not understand me, but I've found there are some friendships that don't need words, and the one I had with Maggie was that kind.

Jakey pointed a chubby finger at me. "He wuvs you."

Maggie petted my neck and held me close. "I love you too, Reginald."

Jakey threw up his short arms, feeling left out.

"And you too, Jakey." Maggie smiled and gathered him to her. "It'll be okay, right Reg?"

I crowed loudly to reassure her.

"Cocky Doodle Doo!"

They both laughed.

AMIDST all the changes on the farm, facing bullies was something I too was still dealing with on a regular basis.

Fighting off Rocky had improved my standing with the ladies but did little to help me along with the bigger roosters.

Biff began shoving me around one night and I took up my battle stance.

"Not here," he said. "I want plenty of room to beat you into oblivion. Meet me in the chicken yard at high noon and we'll settle this like roosters."

I looked at him curiously. "Have you been watching Westerns?"

He blinked back at me blankly.

I knew he couldn't read. Maybe he'd been listening to Jakey playing outside. The little guy was on a cowboy kick lately.

"Alright," I sighed. "High noon it is."

LATE THAT NIGHT, I was awakened by strange noises outside. It sounded like a cat yowling or a baby crying.

Alarmed, I thought it might be Lacey for a moment.

I blearily opened my eyes and looked out of the window toward the house. None of the lights were on. Everyone appeared to be sleeping.

I jumped as the noise started again, this time deepening.

It sounded like some kind of monster outside gnawing on something.

I shuddered as my imagination ran through the possibilities. That was definitely not a baby, or a loon, or anything else I'd ever heard before.

I squinted into the darkness but saw nothing out of the ordinary.

I kept still for several moments, barely breathing, my heart racing as I struggled to hear the noise again.

Even the crickets were silent.

A few minutes later, they resumed their summer song, probably for the last time. It was getting cooler in the evenings, and the seasons would turn soon.

I nestled back into my preferred corner, not far from my dear Reds, and fell back into a restless sleep.

I CRACKED OPEN an eye the next day, feeling awful. All of my physical activities were starting to drain me.

Maggie and Sam came to check on us, as they always did. They never mentioned hearing any noises and neither did any of the others in my flock. Perhaps it had been a nightmare.

I spent the morning with the ladies, regaling them with stories and waiting for the appointed fight time.

The sun shone warmly on us at high noon, but Biff was nowhere to be found.

Not in the coop nor in the yard.

Speedy and I hopped the fence. The others were too heavy to do so.

That's when we noticed the gaping hole in the bottom of it, along with some of Biff's golden feathers.

"What is Biff up to?" my little friend asked. "Did he chicken out and try to escape?"

I looked at Speedy, concerned. "Or perhaps he was dragged away against his will. Did he come in last night?"

I couldn't remember seeing him in the hen house.

Speedy's dark eyes widened. "Not good."

We made our way to the barn and asked the cows.

They hadn't seen him. Neither had the pigs or the geese.

In fact, no one had seen him at all.

"Did you hear anything last night?" I asked.

"I did," trembled Buttercup, her heavy udders shaking along with her. "It sounded big and hungry."

Whatever it was, I suspected it had been snacking on Biff, and that the same fate may have befallen the other missing chickens. So far, only a few of Philomena's feathers had been found. The others had vanished without a trace. No bodies, nothing.

"There are only a few creatures that could do that," Henry told us when we visited his stall. "Foxes, wolves, coyotes, and bobcats."

"Do any of them sound like babies?"

The horse shook its head. "Sometimes they sound like women screaming."

"What I heard sounded like a baby, but then got deeper," I said.

"And there's a hole in our fence now," Speedy added.

"Stay alert," warned Henry. "Something's amiss."

We returned to the yard and told the other roosters, but they didn't believe us, as usual.

"How many of us have to disappear before you start listening?" I groaned in frustration. "First Philomena, then Penelope, Lolita, Bart, and now Biff!"

"That's five chickens, gone!" Speedy spoke up.

I was impressed that someone else besides me could count.

The other boys just stared back at us blankly. The girls shivered.

"We are not islands unto ourselves," I continued. "We need to work together and with the other animals!"

But they wouldn't listen. They thought we were crazy.

"You've been talking to that duck for too long," snapped Sweetie, then stormed out of the hen house.

CHAPTER NINE

Another day, another challenge. This time from Bruce.
I dispensed of him even quicker than I had Rocky.

The girls swooned again and suddenly I was wallowing in more attention than I could handle as a reward for my valiant efforts.

I recited poetry and stories till I was exhausted.

"Speedy! Get down here and help a guy out."

"What?" he peered down from his perch nervously. He had never talked to the ladies. He was terrified of them.

Slacker. It was high time he learned.

It took half an hour to talk him out of the tree, but he finally acquiesced.

The ladies all stared at him.

He looked back, nervous, then took me aside. "What do I say?"

"Just tell them some of those corny jokes. The ones you tell Henry."

"Do you think they'd really like those?"

"Can't hurt to try."

"Alright." He took a deep breath and forged ahead. "What do you call a magic cow?"

The girls looked at each other, then back at him.

"Moodini!"

They chuckled and practiced a little Tae Kwon Duck together, which seemed to loosen Speedy up. Soon he was cracking jokes as often as he did with Henry, and they were all squawking with laughter.

But Speedy's newfound joy was short-lived when Sweetie caught wind of the whole thing and butted his fluffy self in.

He had finally reached the end of his patience. "That's it! Stay away from my ladies, you shrimps! Or I'll kick both your butts."

"Go right ahead," Speedy spat back, drawing himself up to his full, feathery height, which wasn't much.

Still, he was a rather striking rooster, much like myself. Perhaps that's what Sweetie hated most about us. We also had better names. Sweetie was like a boy named Sue. And his frilly feathers didn't help much either. They made it difficult to take him seriously.

He charged us both.

We took up our battle stances as Lucky had shown us.

"*Shi-Jak!*" we yelled, then danced out of the way at the last minute as Sweetie barreled through and crashed into the outer wall of the hen house.

He shook himself off and stood up slowly, angrier than ever.

"You're the instigator," he jabbed his wing at me. "Always stirring things up. I bet you put him up to it!"

I did my best to fend off his attacks, but Sweetie was too strong.

Speedy jumped on his back and started pecking at his head to get him off of me.

He flung Speedy off and sent him flying over the fence.

Sweetie began pounding me into oblivion, striking blow after blow. I feared he meant to kill me this time.

I glanced at Speedy, who had scrambled up a tree, his cowardice getting the better of him.

I looked at the girls, who stood there, appalled.

Everything started to fade when I heard Ginger scream. "You leave our Reginald alone!"

They all jumped on him, kicking and clawing him.

Somehow, I got trapped beneath the entire pile of them, which knocked the wind right out of me.

IN THE MIDST of all the chaos, I heard that horrible noise again. A baby crying, that deepened into something else, something more chilling.

We all froze, suddenly aware of a very large spotted cat looking at us, licking its chops.

"Bobcat!" Speedy screamed.

The girls panicked, running in all directions and clucking for all they were worth.

This confused the cat, which decided to focus on the closest and largest prospect, Sweetie.

As luck would have it, he was half passed out on top of me.

Tarnation, I muttered to myself. What an inconvenient time to get pinned beneath an overweight chicken.

"Go get help!" I yelled at Speedy. "Someone big!"

Speedy nodded and raced off.

The huge cat circled us, looking very hungry.

Sweetie stood up slowly.

"What is that?" he murmured, still dazed.

"It's the reason the other chickens disappeared," I whispered. "Run."

His eyes grew wide and he prepared to bolt.

The cat lunged at us before we could move, sinking its claws into Sweetie's backside.

He shrieked in pain as the feline began to tear his white feathers out.

I leapt on the bobcat's back and sank my talons into him, but to no avail. The animal was completely focused on making Sweetie his next meal.

"Not today!" I told that blasted cat, then jumped on his head and began pecking his face.

If he could fight unfairly, so could I.

That got his attention. The predator flung Sweetie aside and tried to claw me off his face as I pecked at his eyes. I would defend my flock, whatever it took!

Just then, Henry leapt over the fence with Speedy on his back.

"Charge!" my little friend yelled.

I scurried out of the way as quickly as I could.

Henry neighed fiercely and reared up, then began stomping on the bobcat with his hooves.

"Now kick him in the rear!" Speedy commanded.

The horse did, and the cat went sailing into the side of the hen house with a crash. He was knocked cold.

Bill, Melissa, Maggie, and Sam came running to see what the ruckus was all about.

Bill was carrying a shot gun. "What on Earth?"

He glanced around, assessing the situation quickly.

"Martha, call animal control!" he hollered, then studied the passed-out bobcat.

"Sam," he said calmly, "Get the animal trap out of the barn and bring it here. We need to cage it before it wakes up."

"What can we do, Dad?" Maggie asked.

"Make sure the chickens are okay." He set down the shot gun as Sam returned with the cage.

Maggie rushed to check on us. "Oh Reg, what happened to Sweetie?"

He was in bad shape, with deep gashes across his hind quarters.

Maggie began examining his wounds while Bill and Sam moved the unconscious bobcat into the cage without incident, much to everyone's relief.

Speedy and I went to settle down the ladies. The worst was over. We hoped.

Bill stroked Henry's mane and fed him a carrot.

"What was Henry doing out here?" he asked, puzzled. "He rarely leaves his stall."

Speedy sat on the horse's back and crowed triumphantly.

The farmer shook his head in disbelief. "Strangest thing I ever saw."

"They're friends, Dad. They're watching out for one another," Maggie said. "And if these little guys can stand up to their bullies, I can stand up to mine too."

Bill smiled at her. "I'm proud of you, honey."

Maggie smiled back. "I'm proud of them." She shook her finger at her father. "And they are never ending up with the turkeys!"

Speedy lifted his head. "Just where are the turkeys?"

"Trust me, you don't want to know," Henry whinnied.

"They didn't have names," I said and left it at that.

Speedy frowned. "Oh."

LATER, Bill struggled to explain the situation to the astounded animal control officer.

"So, you're telling me a bunch of chickens fought the bobcat off, and then a horse with a rooster on its back flung him into the wall."

Bill nodded. "They seemed to be working together."

"And you saw this?"

"Right at the end," he said.

The man looked at him as if he was crazy. "Are you feelin' okay, buddy?"

Bill raked a hand through his hair and sighed. "We have a newborn in the house."

The man smirked. "That would explain why you look like you haven't slept in a year."

Bill laughed. "It certainly feels that way."

"I have three myself," he smiled. "Alright, we'll have to figure out what to do with the bobcat. There's a sanctuary north of here. Maybe they'd be interested in him."

"As long as it's far from here," Bill said. "We've lost plenty of chickens from that thing's appetite."

"The best thing you can do is reinforce your fencing and keep the bigger animals close. If the horse is protective of them, it might be a good idea to put them closer together."

Bill rubbed his stubbled chin. "You know, that's not a bad idea."

"A guard dog is also a possibility. There are a few large breeds that will protect chickens and other livestock, rather than eat them."

"Like a sheep dog?" Bill asked.

"Yes, some are very good for guarding chickens. So are Great Pyrenees. They're big, but you've got plenty of room here. They're good with kids too."

He left with the cat then, and I could tell Bill was pondering his options.

CHAPTER TEN

The he rest of us roosters pulled together to lead the flock, keeping watch over the hens, worried that Sweetie's days might be numbered.

Bill extended the chicken yard to the horse stalls, giving us a lot more room and neighbors.

Soon, Henry and Speedy were cracking bad jokes all day.

"What happens when a duck flies upside down?" Speedy asked.

"It quacks up!" Henry laughed.

"Good heavens," I protested. "You're killing me, one awful joke at time."

"I don't get it," said Lucky.

Bill also reinforced the fence and cleared the brush nearby to discourage predators from hiding in it. He planned to build a newer hen house as soon as possible.

MAGGIE CAME home from school one day, dancing. "I did it, Reg! I stood up to that bully who was pulling my hair. Can you believe what he told me?"

"What?" Jakey and I asked from our spot beneath our favorite tree.

"He said he liked me." She twisted up her face in disgust. "Ewww!"

Well, who wouldn't? I thought.

Perhaps humans weren't so different from us after all.

Not long after, we welcomed Sweetie back into the coop. He came through the whole ordeal surprisingly unscathed, being the fighter that he is.

"Did you miss me?" he asked.

"Not really," I admitted.

He punched me in the shoulder.

"Ouch."

He was still a jerk, but he was our jerk.

COCKY DOODLE BOO

Something "fowl" is brewing this Halloween...

It's the flock's first fall on the farm and strange things are afoot, including a Were-Chicken! Can Reginald and his fellow roosters protect the ladies and save the day?

Find out more at ReginaldFowl.com or get it here:

http://books2read.com/cockydoodleboo

THANK YOU

Thanks for reading Cocky Doodle Doo! If you enjoyed the book, please take a moment to leave a review. Your opinion matters, and is especially crucial for independent publishers!

If you received the book through a torrenting or file sharing website, please consider purchasing a legal copy. Your purchases are votes of encouragement to keep artists, writers and literate chickens going!

MEET THE AUTHORS

Reginald Fowl is an author and poet, but mostly, he's a proud rooster of some intelligence and perseverance. When he isn't busy writing his memoirs, he likes to solve mysteries, woo the ladies and read stodgy old tomes. You can subscribe to his newsletter and find out more about him at ReginaldFowl.com. You can also find him on his Facebook Page. And what rooster doesn't love Twitter? You find him there too.

Kimberly Gordon is an author, digital artist, and mother of five boys. She lives in a hundred-year-old farmhouse in the Midwest, where she enjoys coming up with outrageous stories to tell to anyone who will listen, including her chickens, who sometimes come up with ideas for their own. Find out what she's up to next on her website and sign up for her newsletter at http://www.kimberlymgordon.com

amazon.com/author/kimberlygordon

bookbub.com/authors/kimberly-gordon

facebook.com/ReginaldFowl

goodreads.com/kimberlymgordon

instagram.com/kimberlygordonauthor

pinterest.com/llynara

twitter.com/Reginald_Fowl

MEET THE PEEPS

Enjoying the world of Reginald and his friends? Here's a list of the cast and crew, to help keep them all straight:

Chickens:
Reginald- our hero, a BB Red Old English Bantam (or Game Fowl)
Sweetie- the not so sweet bully and head rooster; a very large Light Brahma
Speedy -a high strung Silver Duckwing rooster
Biff- a large Buff Ophington rooster
Rocky- a tough Barred Rock rooster

Bruce - a Black Australorpe rooster

Bart - an unfortunately named Buff Orpington hen

Squinty - A large Barred Rock with strange looking eyes. A bit on the slow side.

Ginger - a lovely Rhode Island Red hen

Lucille - a lovely Rhode Island Red hen

Lilah- a lovely Rhode Island Red hen

Philomena- a Black Australorpe hen

Lolita- a Blue Andalusian hen

Foo Foo- A fluffy, Silkie hen whose feathers hang down in her eyes. As a result, she's rather clumsy and not very observant

Princess - a pretty, fluffy Light Brahma hen

Bella - a pretty, fluffy Light Brahma hen

Frankie - a Barred Rock hen

Georgie Girl- a Buff Orpington hen

Myrtle - a Barred Rock hen

Jezebel - a Black Austrolorpe hen

Lulu- a forgetful Blue Andalusian hen with short term memory problems

Penelope- a Blue Andalusian hen

Cows: Beatrice, Buttercup and Moo

Ducks: Lucky- Tae Kwon Duck master

Geese: Hans and Greta- mated pair of geese

Horses:

Henry- an old steed

Betsy- his mate who passed away

Humans:

Maggie- the little red headed girl who names Reginald and teaches him how to read and write

Sam- her other brother

Melissa- her snotty teen-aged know-it-all older sister

Jakey- a toddler, Maggie's little brother

Lacey- the baby

Bill- the farmer
Martha - farmer's wife
Roger- a bully at school
No names: pigs, turkeys, a few former cows

MEET THE BREEDS

A quick guide to the different breeds used in the story.

Chickens:
  Black Australorpes - A large meat and egg bird with a good disposition. They are very hardy and make great parents.
  Barred Rock - A black and white striped bird, very striking. They tend to chatter all day long, which can get noisy.
  Bantam - A small type of chicken, very light weight, beautiful and great egg layer. Most tend to be calm.
  Blue Andalusian - Not actually blue, more grayish. Not considered a good meat or egg bird, but interesting and beautiful.

Light Brahma - Gorgeous, hardy, fluffy birds with feathers on their feet and a doubly thick coat of feathers on their bodies. Great in cooler climates, they tend to suffer in hotter ones.

Buff Orphington - Large golden birds. Very pretty. Good for meat and eggs.

Rhode Island Red - Fantastic egg bird, also fine for meat (So I've heard! Shocking!) Very common as they are easy to keep. Some can be aggressive.

BB Red Old English Game Fowl - A beautiful, breed of show chickens of the Bantam variety. They are small, strong and muscular. They tend to be calm and fast learners. Reginald (*moi*) is from this breed.

Silver Duckwing - A beautiful Bantam variety, also considered an Old English Game Fowl, with large comb and striking feathers. Speedy is one of these.

Silkie - A pretty and very loving breed with poofs of feathers on their heads and very silky feathers on their bodies. They are fantastic parents to any breed and will even mother chicks from other species.

Ducks:

Peking- Great egg layers, can be quite aggressive. Note: Not many of them know Tae Kwon Duck!

Manufactured by Amazon.ca
Bolton, ON

25906933R00039